This DangerSpot book belongs to:

- - - - - - - - - - - - - - - - - - - - - - - - - - - - - - - - - -

Published in 2004 by DangerSpot Books Ltd.
Old Bank House,
High Street,
Laxfield,
Woodbridge,
Suffolk.
IP13 8DX.

Printed by Proost NV, Turnhout, Belgium.

ISBN 0-9546565-2-0

# Fire in the Fryer

## Hedley Griffin

DangerSpot Books Ltd.

It was a busy-bee, hot, sunny morning.

Harey, the hare-brained rabbit, was busy in the kitchen making tea.

Meanwhile, Scampi the cat and Chips the dog were out in the garden, passing the time watching the butterflies feeding on the buddleia bush.

'They're always so difficult to stroke!' she said.

'Don't touch the fluttery ones,' said Chips. 'They sting!'

'No, they don't, you silly. They are butterflies. They're lovely.

The ones that sting are the wasps and bees,' she said.

'They go "Buzz, Buzz!"'

'Oh, yes. Buzz, Buzz!' said Chips, thoughtfully,
as he relaxed in a wooden deck chair
and gazed at the fluffy, white clouds in the sky.

'Those clouds look like bones!' he said.

Harey gave Scampi her tea.

He then put the other hot mug of tea on the arm of Chip's chair,
which was not very sensible.

'Look like bones?' asked Harey, suddenly looking up at the sky.

As he did so, he knocked Chip's tea over.

'Arghh!' screamed Chips, as he leapt into the air.

He hopped around the garden holding his scalded thigh while Scampi chased after him with a sponge of cold water and a towel.

'That'll stop it swelling and hurting so much,' said Scampi.

'Let's have a barbecue?' Harey suggested.

'Yeeah!' said everyone at once.

'...And shall we have chips with it?' he added.

'Double yeah, yeah!' said everyone at once again.

'Ok! I'll go and prepare it,' said Harey,

rushing off like a hare-brained rabbit as always.

'Could we invite Pillow the parrot?' asked Chips.

'Yes, why not. He doesn't get out much,' said Scampi.

'So, why's he called "Pillow"?' asked Chips.

'Because he's full of feathers!' giggled Scampi.

A little later, Pillow, Scampi and Chips found Harey with the barbecue.

'I can't get the coals to light!' said Harey.

'Have you put some barbecue lighter fuel on them?' asked Scampi.

'Oh no, of course. I'll go and get some,' he said, rushing off into the garage.

He soon came back with a can of petrol.
'I couldn't find the proper barbecue
lighter fuel, but this will do instead,'
said Harey, splashing petrol over the coals.
'That's not petrol, is it?' Scampi nervously
asked, smelling the fumes and fearing
the worse.
'Yes, but that'll be alright!' said Harey,
striking a match.

'What? No!' she shouted, as the barbecue exploded in a ball of flames, and everyone got scorched. Fortunately, nobody was badly hurt.

'You should never set light to anything using petrol, you hare-brained rabbit!' scolded Scampi.

'No, I don't think you should have done that!' advised Chips.

'Who's a silly bunny, then?' added Pillow.

They had just finished cleaning themselves up when Scampi noticed smoke coming from the kitchen.

'What's that burning smell?' she asked.

'Oops! I think I may have left the deep-frying oil pan on the cooker for the chips,' said Harey.

'Perhaps, I should go and check it?'

'What?' Scampi shrieked again.

'You should never just put the oil pan on and leave it like that!'

Harey was already rushing into the kitchen where he found flames shooting from the oil-fryer. He quickly turned round and picked up a bowl of water from the sink. He was just about to throw the water over the fire when Scampi quickly stopped him.

'Don't ever use a bowl of water on an oil-fryer fire!' screamed Scampi, switching off the gas and placing a damp cloth over the pan.

Immediately the flames disappeared.

'You must only use a damp cloth or a fire blanket. Otherwise, you'll just spread the fire all over the kitchen,' she warned. 'You could have had the whole house alight.'

'And more important, we're not going to get our burger and chips now, are we!' moaned Chips.

'Never mind, I'll go and make us a sandwich!' said Harey,
rushing off like a hare-brained rabbit as usual.

'Now, what is he going to get up to next?' Scampi wondered.

And so do we!

# Place the DangerSpot stickers around your home as a reminder of the dangers and keep your children safe!

Never leave hot drinks where children can knock them over. Remember, a child's skin is much more sensitive than an adult's.

In the event of a burn or scald immediately apply cold water.

Never use petrol for anything else other than its intended use. Make sure the cans are placed beyond a child's reach.

Hide matches away from children.

Learn about dangerous insects, reptiles, sea creatures etc., especially when traveling abroad.

Never leave a heating chip pan unattended. If it should ever catch fire, use a damp cloth or fire blanket, **not** water.

Always keep a fire blanket in the kitchen or elsewhere in the home.

Try to prevent children rushing around thoughtlessly, especially through a kitchen where most accidents can happen.

Fit several approved smoke alarms in your home on each floor.

Information supplied by The Royal Society for the Prevention of Accidents. www.rospa.com